ON A TRAIN JOURNEY

This book belongs to:

FINDING THE STATION

Stations, big or small, are always well sign-posted to help travellers get there easily. Here, the way to the station is shown as part of a large city centre direction sign. In which city is there a station called Waverley?

I-Spy for 10
Double with answer

This station shows the way to the station car park.
I-Spy for 5

In the country, you may even find a direction sign fixed to a five-barred gate.
I-Spy for 15

Your first sight of the station might be looking down on it like this.
I-Spy for **15**

Many railway stations have large car parks.

I-Spy for **5**
Double if the station is a Parkway built specially to serve motorists from a wide area.

You might arrive to find yourself under a canopy which protects travellers from the rain.
I-Spy for **10**

Large stations always have queues of taxis arriving and departing.
I-Spy for **5**

STATION SIGNS

Outside the station there is usually a large sign showing its name, often with the famous double-arrow symbol. The sign is usually mounted on a tall pole so that it can be seen from some distance away. Do you know where Wanborough is?

Wanborough

I-Spy for **5**
Double with answer

Welcome to ScotRail Fort William

Many stations also have a 'Welcome' sign like this.
I-Spy for **10**

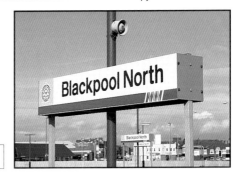

Blackpool North

All stations have nameboards on the platform so that travellers arriving by train can see where they are.
I-Spy for **5**

There are more than 2400 stations on the National Railways network, ranging in size from great mainline termini in cities, like this one...
I-Spy for 5

...to small rural stations set in the midst of beautiful countryside.
I-Spy for 10

And there are even some stations which are completely underground.
I-Spy for 10

PLATFORMS

The station you travel from could have been built at any time in the past 150 years. What a contrast there is between the concourse of a big Victorian main line station...
I-Spy for 5

...or the platform buildings of a traditional wayside country station.
I-Spy for 10

And then there is the ultra-modern waiting shelter on a new station.
I-Spy for 10

There are many different types of bridge spanning the railway tracks. This
one is for pedestrians to cross from one side of a main line to the other.
I-Spy for 15

And this one carries road traffic over the railway lines.
I-Spy for 5

An overbridge is the usual way in which travellers can cross the lines at a busy railway station. This graceful design is made of iron and positioned under the station's vast overall roof.
I-Spy for 5

This much more angular design is made of concrete and is open to the elements.
I-Spy for 5

This design of overbridge, however, is completely covered to keep people dry.
I-Spy for 10

Large stations always have a travel centre where you can buy tickets and make reservations, as well as pick up leaflets and get all the information you need to plan your train journeys.
I-Spy for 5

There are also special information kiosks at some stations.
I-Spy for 10

And many stations have self-service ticket machines to speed up buying your ticket.
I-Spy for 10

9

DEPARTURE TIME

Full details of the times that trains depart and their destinations are displayed on large dot-matrix indicator boards at major stations.
I-Spy for 5

Train departure times are also listed alphabetically by destination on poster boards.
I-Spy for 5

Details of the next departure from each platform are shown on television monitors.
I-Spy for 10

Most travellers arrive at a station with time to spare before they catch their train. So stations are excellent places for traders to sell a wide range of goods. It also makes travelling more enjoyable if you can make last-minute purchases at the station. Here are just a few of the retail outlets you can see at stations:

This bookstall sells newspapers, magazines, videos, stationery, sweets, soft drinks, as well as books etc.
I-Spy for 5

Most stations have at least one place to buy food and drinks. Large stations have fast-food counters where you can get burgers and pizzas.
I-Spy for 5

As its name suggests, this shop sells socks and tights. There are also shops which specialize in ties and in underwear.
I-Spy for 15

A Bureau de Change, where travellers can obtain foreign currency, is a boon to anyone going abroad.
I-Spy for 10

Britain's railways have had their own independent police force since the very beginning. Originally, railway policemen also acted as signalmen and controlled the movement of trains. Even today, some railway staff refer to the signalman as 'bobby'. Do you know why policemen are called bobbies?

I-Spy for **10**
Double with answer

Public telephones at stations let travellers keep in touch with home or work.
I-Spy for **5**

Photograph booths can be useful for anyone needing a picture for a travelpass or a passport.
I-Spy for **5**

Trains are not the only form of wheeled transport you'll find moving around at stations. Parcel trolleys, too, are joined up into long 'trains' and pulled along by small motorized vehicles of different shapes and sizes.
I-Spy for 5

A number of main line stations have courtesy buggies like this one to take disabled or unwell travellers and their luggage to or from the train in comfort.
I-Spy for 20

Odd-looking vehicles like this are used to refill the water tanks in buffet cars and toilets between trips.
I-Spy for 15

And, of course, there are always plenty of self-help luggage trolleys to save travellers having to carry heavy suitcases and bags by hand.
I-Spy for 5

SITTING PRETTY

It's always nice to be able to take the weight off your feet and sit down while waiting for your train. Modern station seats are made from metal and look like this.
I-Spy for **5**

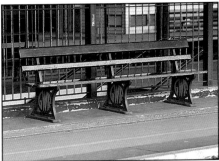

Older station seats are made from wood and cast iron, and sometimes carry the initials of the railway company that has made them. This seat has GWR in its base. To which railway did it originally belong?

I-Spy for **10**
Double with answer

Flowers also help make a station even more pleasant and cheerful. Many stations have floral displays in hanging baskets, while others feature plants in a trough like this one.
I-Spy for **10**

Many trains have automatic-opening sliding doors operated by press-buttons. The doors are in the overall control of the Guard or Senior Conductor. Here is the button to open the door from the outside of the train.
I-Spy for 10

And this shows the buttons to open (green) and close (red) the door from inside the carriage.
I-Spy for 10

There are automatic doors at the ends of carriages, too. They are activated by a pressure pad in the floor just in front of the door.
I-Spy for 5

Many trains convey both First Class and Standard accommodation. InterCity First Class has 46 or 48 seats arranged in a 2 + 1 formation across the central aisle.
I-Spy for 5

Standard InterCity carriages have about 76 seats in a 2 + 2 arrangement and are air conditioned, double glazed, and have wall-to-wall carpets.
I-Spy for 5

Lightweight Pacer trains for local services have an interior layout which is similar to that of a bus.
I-Spy for 10

Tip-up seats in the vestibule are a feature of the InterCity 225 high-speed electric train's Standard accommodation.
I-Spy for 10

Many InterCity trains carry a restaurant car where travellers can enjoy a full meal, with wine, while on the move.
I-Spy for 5

Hot snacks and a wide variety of light refreshments are available from the buffet car.
I-Spy for 5

On many trains which do not convey a buffet car, there is a trolley service of drinks and snacks brought to the traveller's seat.
I-Spy for 10

A phone can be found on many express trains. It takes a standard phonecard and can be used for outgoing calls.
I-Spy for 10 – double if you see someone using the phone

Elegant table settings with individual lamps are a feature of First Class Pullman services. Pullman trains take their name from their originator, George Mortimer Pullman. What nationality was he?

I-Spy for 10
Double with answer

First Class seats usually have head-rest covers bearing the name of the train company operating the service.
I-Spy for 5

Trains are homes on wheels for travellers during their journey. Here are just a few things you'll find inside the average railway carriage:

A toilet with washbasin, soap, and towels so you can freshen up on a long journey.
I-Spy for **5**

Litter bins for your rubbish to help keep the train tidy.
I-Spy for **5**

Luggage racks above the seats and at the ends of carriages, as you can see here.
I-Spy for **5**

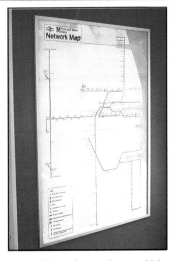

A map of the rail network over which the train runs. Do you know which is the most northerly station in Britain?

Fire extinguishers located at the end of a carriage.
I-Spy for 10

I-Spy for 15
Double with answer

The alarm handle to stop the train in an emergency.
I-Spy for 5

Britain's train companies have around 130,000 staff working to make your journey a pleasant one. You won't see them all, of course, but here are a few you may encounter:

On the platform the Station Supervisor blows his whistle and gives the guard the right-away for the train to leave.
I-Spy for 5

And the driver starts the train out of the station.
I-Spy for 5

On many local services, which serve unstaffed stations, the Conductor Guard issues tickets from a portable machine.
I-Spy for 10

While, on InterCity trains, the Senior Conductor checks tickets and helps travellers with journey information, as well as performing his or her duties as guard.
I-Spy for **10**

On-train staff, in their distinctive uniforms, may often be seen waiting to greet passengers as they join the train. In this picture you can see staff from Great Western Trains.
I-Spy for **10**

Although a lot of track maintenance is done at night, you are sure to see men at work on the lines during the day. They wear bright-orange high-visibility clothing so that the train drivers can see them from a long way off.
I-Spy for **10**

One of the joys of train travel (especially if you have *I-Spy on a Train Journey* to hand) is all the places and things of interest that you can look for through the carriage window as the train rushes through town and country. Here is a selection. See how many of these you can I-Spy and then look out for others of your own.

I-Spy 5 for each

Cathedrals and churches, with their high steeples and towers.

Tower blocks of flats in big cities.

The seashore, with holidaymakers strolling along the golden sands.

THROUGH THE WINDOW

A windmill – or a watermill.

A water tower.

A golf course – or another sports venue.

A deer park.

Sailing dinghies – or another water sport.

A gas holder.

Cooling towers.

A field of poppies.

The winding gear from a disused coal mine.

Pigs – or any other farm animal.

BY THE WATER

Many railway lines run close to the seashore or near to a stretch of inland water, such as this loch set among hills and glimpsed from the train.

I-Spy for 15

This train is at a station which serves a harbour, and a large ferry boat can be seen behind it.

I-Spy for 15

This train is running along the edge of an estuary, next to the pleasure craft moored there.
I-Spy for 15

Here, a large dockyard, with its tall cranes, can be seen from the train.
I-Spy for 20

OVER AND UNDER

When railways were built, they often required massive engineering works to carry them across the land. Tunnels like these were cut through the hillside when it was not possible to go over or around the obstacle. Which is the longest railway tunnel in Britain?

*I-Spy for **10** – double with answer*

Embankments are raised earthworks constructed to take the line across a gap in the land.
*I-Spy for **5***

Railway lines are carried across valleys, rivers, and roads by a variety of bridges and viaducts. This graceful viaduct is constructed of stones and has many arches.
I-Spy for 10

A single arch is sufficient to carry this bridge over a minor country road.
I-Spy for 5

BRIDGES AND VIADUCTS

This bridge is most unusual in that it carries both rail (on the upper deck) and road (on the lower) across a river.
I-Spy for 30

You may see a completely different type of bridge from a train – one that carries a motorway. But you can also I-Spy a motorway from a bridge carrying a train over it.
I-Spy for 10

Express trains run at up to 125 miles an hour (200 km/h). They cause air turbulence when passing through stations, and anyone standing too close to the edge of the platform could be swept off their feet and injured. Yellow lines are painted along the length of the platform a safe distance from the edge, and signs like this one are displayed warning travellers to stay back.
*I-Spy for **10***

Overhead electricity cables carry 25 000 volts and can be very dangerous if you get too near to them. This warning sign is fixed to the poles that support the wires as well as to fences bordering the railway lines.
*I-Spy for **10***

Where lines are electrified using the third-rail system, you will see this sign, which has the same design but a slightly different wording.
*I-Spy for **10**
Double if it is combined with a sign warning passengers not to cross the line, like this one.*

31

While trains are at a station being serviced between duties, a sign like this is fixed to the cab to warn the driver not to move it.
I-Spy for **20**

At a terminus station, buffer stops show drivers where the end of the platform is so they can halt their trains at the right place.
I-Spy for **10**

Old-style semaphore signals are rapidly being replaced on main lines but can still be seen on some secondary routes. The two signals on this gantry are set at danger.
I-Spy for 15

Semaphore signals and points are worked by rods and wires connected to levers in manually operated signal-boxes such as the one shown above right.
I-Spy for 15

Where the track layout at a station is not large enough to require a signalbox, the levers are worked from a ground frame, usually at the end of the platform, like this one.
I-Spy for 25

Modern signals have coloured electric lights and are worked from large signalling centres which control many miles of track. This signal has three aspects: red (as shown) means stop; yellow tells the driver to go but be ready to stop at the next signal; green means go.
I-Spy for 5

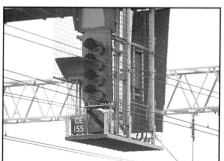

Colour light signals, which control lines through the centre of a large station, are usually suspended above the tracks. This signal has four aspects: the extra one is there to show double yellow which tells the driver to be ready to stop at the second signal ahead.
I-Spy for 5

Electrified lines use either a 25 000 volt a.c. overhead system or a 750 volt d.c. third-rail method. Virtually all high-speed routes are electrified with overhead wires.
I-Spy for **10**

The arm which collects the electricity from the overhead wires and draws it into the locomotive is called a pantograph. When the locomotive is not in use, the pantograph is normally lowered.
I-Spy for **10**

The third-rail system is found mainly on the former Southern Railway lines in south-eastern England. The train has a cast-iron pick-up shoe mounted on a bogie that takes electricity from an extra rail set beside the tracks.
I-Spy for **15**

The maximum speed a train may travel over the various sections of any route depends upon many factors, such as how curved the line is or how many points and crossings there are. Permanent speed restrictions are shown as a figure which is the maximum permissible speed in miles per hour. Some are cut-out metal numerals like this.
I-Spy for **10**
Double if you see one with arrows indicating that the restriction applies to the tracks on both sides of the sign.

Speed restrictions are also shown on metal signs like this one, which warns of the 30 mph limit over a viaduct ahead.
I-Spy for **10**

The InterCity 225 high-speed electric train has a top speed capacity of 140 miles an hour (225 km/h). It runs on Great North Eastern Railway's route from London King's Cross to Leeds, York, Newcastle, Edinburgh, and Glasgow.
I-Spy for 10

The InterCity 125 is the fastest diesel train in the world. It has a top operating speed of 125 miles an hour (200 km/h) and works over routes of four different train companies from Scotland to Penzance in Cornwall.
I-Spy for 5

The 5000 hp Class 90 electric locomotive works high-speed services on Virgin Trains' West Coast route from London Euston to the West Midlands, north-west England, and Glasgow.
I-Spy for 10

Electric multiple units (EMUs) have no separate locomotive but the power equipment is contained within one of the carriages. Here are four different types of EMU:

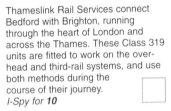

South West Trains' Class 442 Wessex Electrics have a top speed of 100 miles per hour (160 km/h) and run from London to Southampton, Bournemouth, and Weymouth. Which station in London do they use?

I-Spy for 10 – double with answer

Thameslink Rail Services connect Bedford with Brighton, running through the heart of London and across the Thames. These Class 319 units are fitted to work on the over-head and third-rail systems, and use both methods during the course of their journey.
I-Spy for 10

Class 321 units work on a number of important commuter routes north and east of London. This one is operated by Silverlink Train Services.
I-Spy for 10

The Class 365 Networker Express units operate suburban and longer-distance services over Connex South Eastern Lines in London and Kent.
I-Spy for 10

Diesel trains like these operate on non-electrified lines throughout Britain, providing services on local and long-distance routes from the Scottish Highlands to the West Country.

The Class 158 is a luxury, air-conditioned, 90-mile-per-hour (145-km/h) diesel train that offers a high standard of comfort, and operates on the more important routes.
I-Spy for 10

The Class 156 diesel trains generally run on longer-distance routes, including many superbly scenic lines such as the one shown here.
I-Spy for 10

The lightweight Pacer trains, with their bus-type bodies, are used on local and rural services.
I-Spy for 10

Virgin Trains use Class 87 electric locomotives with a top speed of 110 miles per hour (175 km/h) on West Coast services.
I-Spy for 10

Electric locomotive no. 89001 is unique. The prototype of a class intended for the East Coast main line, InterCity 225s were used instead. Now it is operated by Great North Eastern Railway.
I-Spy for 30

Class 37 diesel locomotives are used mainly on freight trains.
I-Spy for 15
Double if you see one working a passenger train.

You won't go far without seeing a freight train. This one is made up of tank wagons. Tank wagons have been built to carry various cargoes including petrol, liquid gas, and chemicals.
I-Spy for 10

A single freight train can carry the equivalent of many lorry loads safely and without harming the environment. Coal is carried in hopper wagons made up into merry-go-round trains, so called because they work in a continuous circuit between pit and power station.
I-Spy for 10

A less familiar sight is this load of timber being conveyed on a freight train in the Scottish Highlands.
I-Spy for 20

Eurostars are high-speed electric trains that link Britain with continental Europe via the Channel Tunnel. They take current from the third rail in Britain and from overhead wires in France and Belgium, travelling at speeds of up to 186 mph (300 km/h).
I-Spy for 30

If you're travelling abroad by air, you can often take the train to the plane. This is the Heathrow Express, a new fast link between London, Paddington, and Heathrow Airport. It uses 100 mph (160 km/h) Class 332 electric trains.
I-Spy for 20

And here is the Stansted Skytrain operated by West Anglia Great Northern Railway. It runs from London Liverpool Street to a railway station in the heart of the airport terminal building at Stansted.
I-Spy for 20

While travelling, you'll see trains belonging to many different railway companies. As you approach London along certain routes, you're bound to run alongside a London Underground train. When was the first completely underground electric 'tube' railway in London opened?

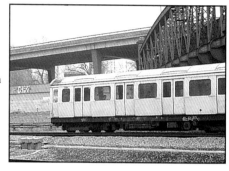

I-Spy for 10
Double with answer

Or you could catch a glimpse of a train on the Docklands Light Rail network which serves this developing area to the east of the City of London.
I-Spy for 15

Steam locomotives were last used in regular service in 1968, but many have been preserved by enthusiasts. Some are allowed to run over Railtrack lines, while others operate on privately owned lines. Many old locomotives are kept at the National Railway Museum. Where is it?

I-Spy for 15
Double with answer

INSIGNIA

Britain's railways are run by many different train companies (a train-operating company is referred to in the industry as a TOC or toc). Each has its own distinctive logo. Here is a large selection of the names that you may see on the side of a locomotive or carriage, on a station nameboard, or even on a poster or a leaflet.
I-Spy 10 for each one that you spot

Anglia Railways ☐

Central Trains ☐

Chiltern Railways ☐

Connex South Eastern ☐

Docklands Light Rail ☐

Eurostar ☐

English Welsh and Scottish Railway ☐

Gatwick Express ☐

Great Eastern Railway ☐

Great North Eastern Railway ☐

Great Western Trains

Heathrow Express

Midland Mainline

LTS Rail

Silverlink Train Services

North Western Trains

Thames Trains

South West Trains

Virgin Trains

Thameslink Rail

Wales & West Passenger Trains

West Anglia Great Northern Railway

Write down the name of any other train company you've seen.
I-Spy 10 for each

JOURNEY'S END

If you are being met at your destination, the arrivals indicator board will tell the person waiting for you when you train is due.
I-Spy for 5

The way out of the station is always clearly marked.
I-Spy for 5

The tracks into many city centre stations are carried above the streets on a low viaduct. The spaces beneath the arches are often used as warehouses and workshops by small businesses.
I-Spy for 15

Journey's end for some passengers may be a welcome drink at one of the many station inns, or other public houses which have a railway name.

I-Spy for **10**
Double if the sign shows a locomotive or a train.

Or you may be staying at a Railway Hotel. These were usually originally built by the railway companies themselves but are all now in other ownership.

I-Spy for **10**

INDEX

Answers

Stations: Waverley is in Edinburgh.
Outside the station: Wanborough is near Guildford.
Railway police: Guildford.
Pullman Services: Bobbies are named after Sir Robert Peel (1788–1850), creator of the modern police force.
Station seats: GWR are the initials of the Great Western Railway. Pullman was George Mortimer Pullman.
American Rail network: Thurso is the most northerly station in Britain.
Tunnels: The Severn Tunnel is the longest tunnel in Britain.
EMUs: Wessex Electrics use American.
London Underground: The first underground electric tube railway was the City & South London, opened in 1890.
Steam locomotives: The National Railway Museum is in York.

© I-Spy Limited 1998

ISBN 1 85671 195 1

Michelin Tyre Public Limited Company
Edward Hyde Building, 38 Clarendon Road, Watford, Herts WD1 1SX

MICHELIN and the Michelin Man are Registered Trademarks of Michelin.

A CIP record for this title is available from the British Library.

Edited by Neil Curtis. Designed by Richard Garratt.

The Publisher gratefully acknowledges the contribution of Peter Greenland Photography who provided many of the photographs in this I-Spy book. The Publisher also gratefully acknowledges the co-operation and assistance of British Rail, and in particular Mike Bowler of British Railways Board, in producing the first edition. Grateful thanks are extended to all the train companies who supplied pictures for this new edition, and to Mike Bowler once again for his assistance in revising it.

Colour reproduction by Anglia Colour.

Printed in Spain by Graficromo SA.